sundance

**LITTLE READER
TWIN TEXTS**

A Day at
the Beach

Written by Jane Keys
Illustrated by Carol Daniel

Content Strand: Earth Science
Focus: Recycling

It was a beautiful day.

We wanted to go
to the beach for a picnic.

But when we got there,
it was a mess.
People had left cans
and bottles everywhere.

"Let's go somewhere else,"
I said.

"But this is my favorite
spot," said Mom.

"Let's clean it up,"
said Dad.
"We can put the bottles
and cans in the trash can.
It won't take long."

Soon the beach was clean.

"Now let's have our picnic,"
I said.

We ate our lunch
and made sand castles.

Then Dad said,
"Let's clean up
and go for a swim!"

"Me too!" said Rosie.